PIANO
L
R

CW00349484

WISE PUBLICATIONS
part of The Music Sales Group
London / New York / Paris / Sydney / Copenhagen /
Berlin / Madrid / Hong Kong / Tokyo

COLDPLAY

MYLO XYLOTO

Published by
Wise Publications
14-15 Berners Street, London W1T 3LJ, UK.

Exclusive Distributors:
Music Sales Limited
Distribution Centre, Newmarket Road,
Bury St Edmunds, Suffolk IP33 3YB, UK.
Music Sales Pty Limited
20 Resolution Drive, Caringbah, NSW 2229, Australia.

Order No. AM1004190
ISBN: 978-1-78038-383-5
This book © Copyright 2011 Wise Publications,
a division of Music Sales Limited.

Edited by Jenni Norey.
Music arranged by Derek Jones.
Music processed by Paul Ewers Music Design.

Printed in the EU.

MYLO XYLOTO

Words & Music by Chris Martin, Guy Berryman, Jon Buckland,
Will Champion & Brian Eno

HURTS LIKE HEAVEN

Words & Music by Chris Martin, Guy Berryman, Jon Buckland,
Will Champion & Brian Eno

-ten up in mark-er on a fac-to-ry sign___ "I strug-gle with the feel-ing that my

life is-n't mine." It's so cold, it's so cold.___

It's so cold, it's so cold.___ See the ar-row they shot try'n' to

tear us a-part.___ Take the fire from my bel-ly and the beat from my heart.___

Still I won't let go._____ Still I won't let go_____ of

you._____

Ooh._____ 'Cause you do.__

Oh,

you_____ use your heart as a weap-on._____ And it hurts_____ like heav-en._____

(Guitar solo ad lib. on D.S.)

soul._____ I'll be armed____ with a spray can soul._____ And

you._____

Ooh._____ Oh,_____ 'Cause

Whoa._____

14

Whoa._____ Yeah, it's   true.   When

you   use your heart as a weap-on_____ then it hurts____ like heav-en._____

_____ *Instrumental ad lib.*

Repeat ad lib. to fade

15

PARADISE

Words & Music by Chris Martin, Guy Berryman, Jon Buckland, Will Champion & Brian Eno

CHARLIE BROWN

Words & Music by Chris Martin, Guy Berryman, Jon Buckland,
Will Champion & Brian Eno

lu - mi -nous and   wired,___

we'll be glow - ing   in   the   dark.___

♩ = 80 Rubato

US AGAINST THE WORLD

Words & Music by Chris Martin, Guy Berryman, Jon Buckland,
Will Champion & Brian Eno

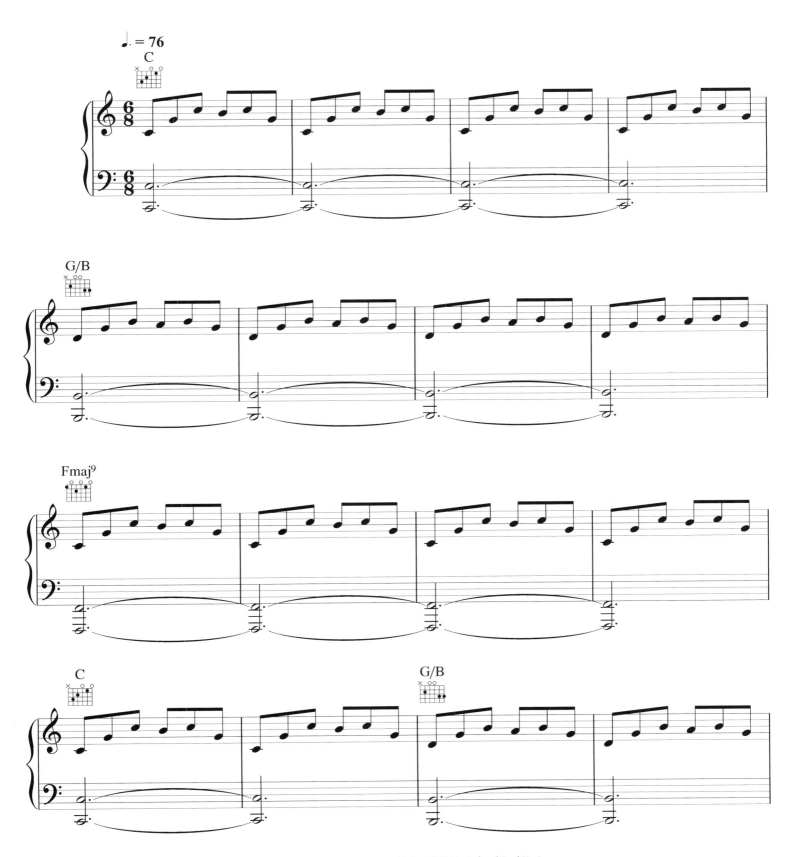

34

38

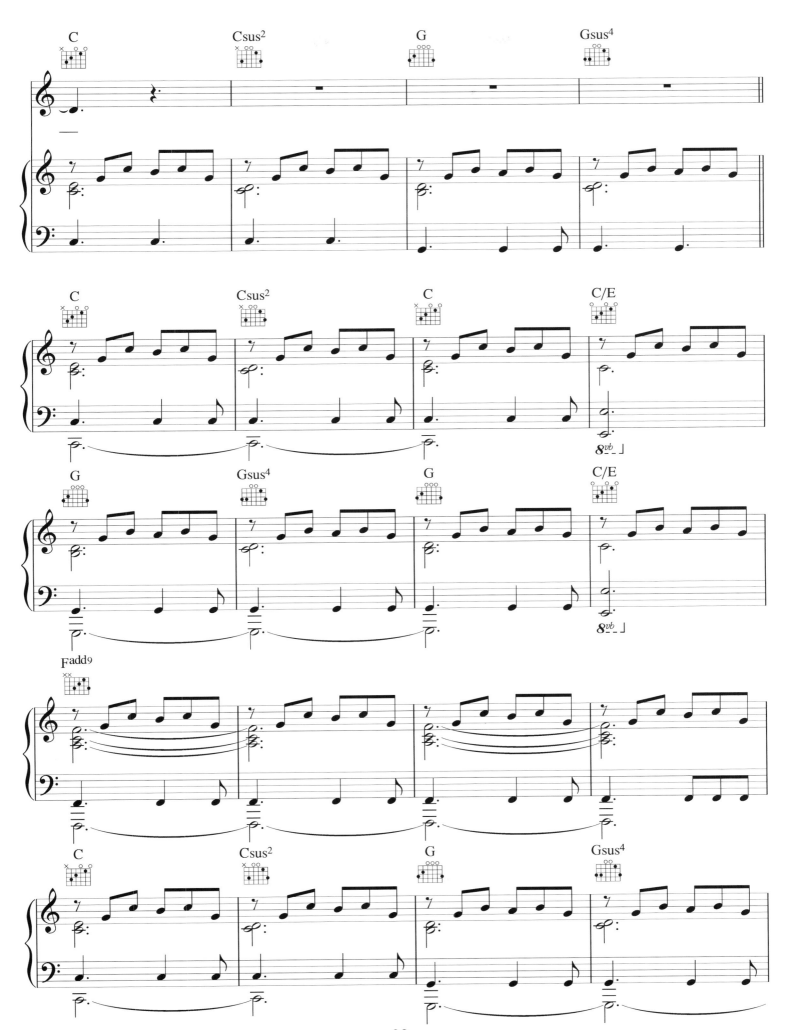

Through cha - os_____ as it swirls.

It's us a - gainst the world.

Through cha - os_____ as it swirls.

It's us a - gainst the world.

M.M.I.X.

Words & Music by Chris Martin, Guy Berryman, Jon Buckland,
Will Champion & Brian Eno

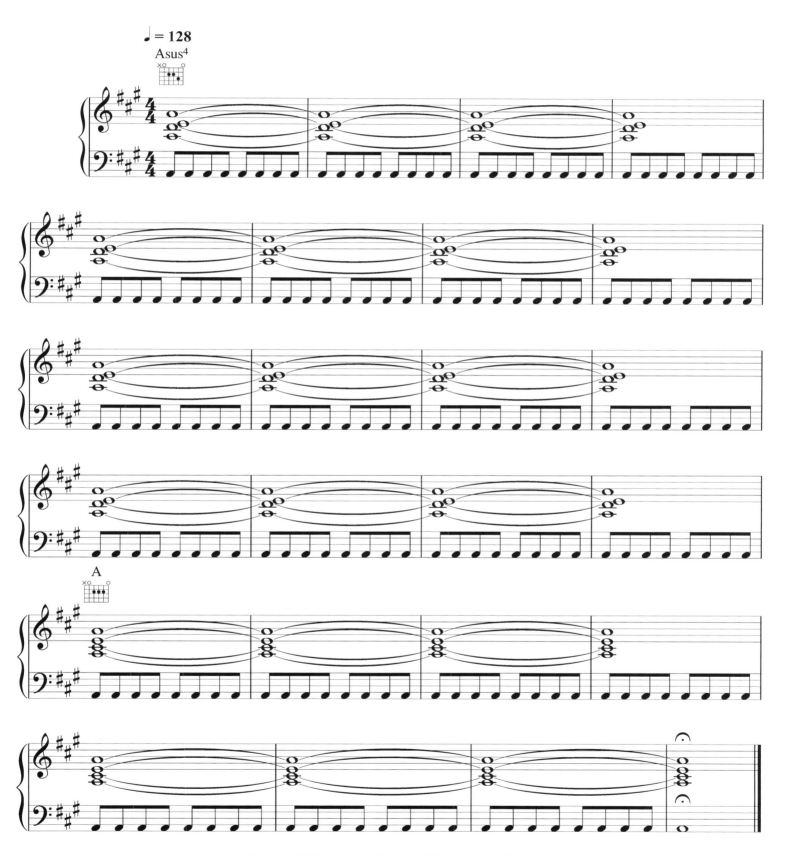

EVERY TEARDROP IS A WATERFALL

Words & Music by Chris Martin, Guy Berryman, Jon Buckland, Will Champion, Brian Eno

2. I turn the mu - sic__ up, I got my re - cords on. From un - der - neath the__ rub - ble, sing a re - bel__ song. Don't want to see an - oth - er gen - er - a - tion__ drop, I'd ra - ther be a__ com - ma than

45

MAJOR MINUS

Words & Music by Chris Martin, Guy Berryman, Jon Buckland, Will Champion & Brian Eno

1. They got one eye watch-ing you,___ and
2. They got one eye watch-ing you,___ and

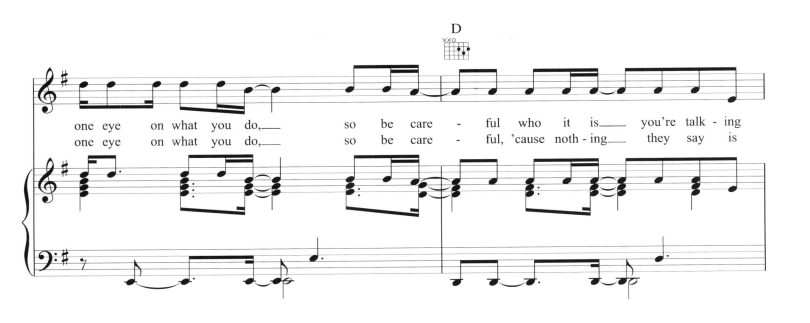

one eye on what you do,___ so be care - ful who it is___ you're talk - ing
one eye on what you do,___ so be care - ful, 'cause noth - ing___ they say is

to. They got one eye watch - ing you,___
true. But then___ don't be - lieve a word;___ it's just

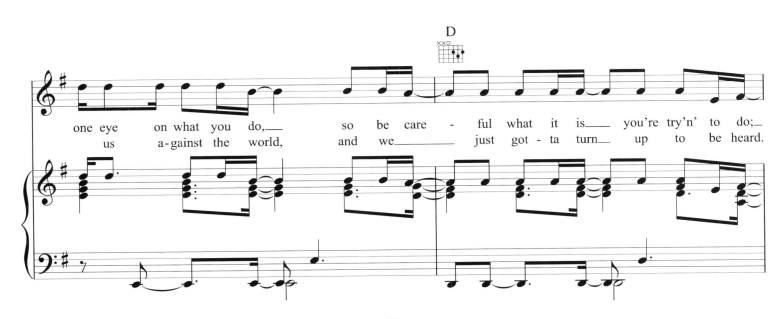

one eye on what you do,___ so be care - ful what it is___ you're try'n' to do;___
us a - gainst the world, and we___ just got - ta turn___ up to be heard.

senza ped.

Em⁷

Bm⁷

Guitar solo

Em⁷

Bm⁷

1.

2.

54

Ooh, ooh._____ Ooh, ooh._____ Got

one eye on the road_ and one on you._ Ooh, ooh._____ Ooh, ooh._____

Got one eye on the road_ and one on you.

55

U.F.O.

Words & Music by Chris Martin, Guy Berryman, Jon Buckland,
Will Champion & Brian Eno

58

Ooh.___

Ooh.___

Ooh.___

PRINCESS OF CHINA

Words & Music by Chris Martin, Guy Berryman, Jon Buckland,
Will Champion & Brian Eno

Once up-on a time we fell a-part. You're hold-ing in your hands the two____ halves of my heart.

Oh.____ Oh.____

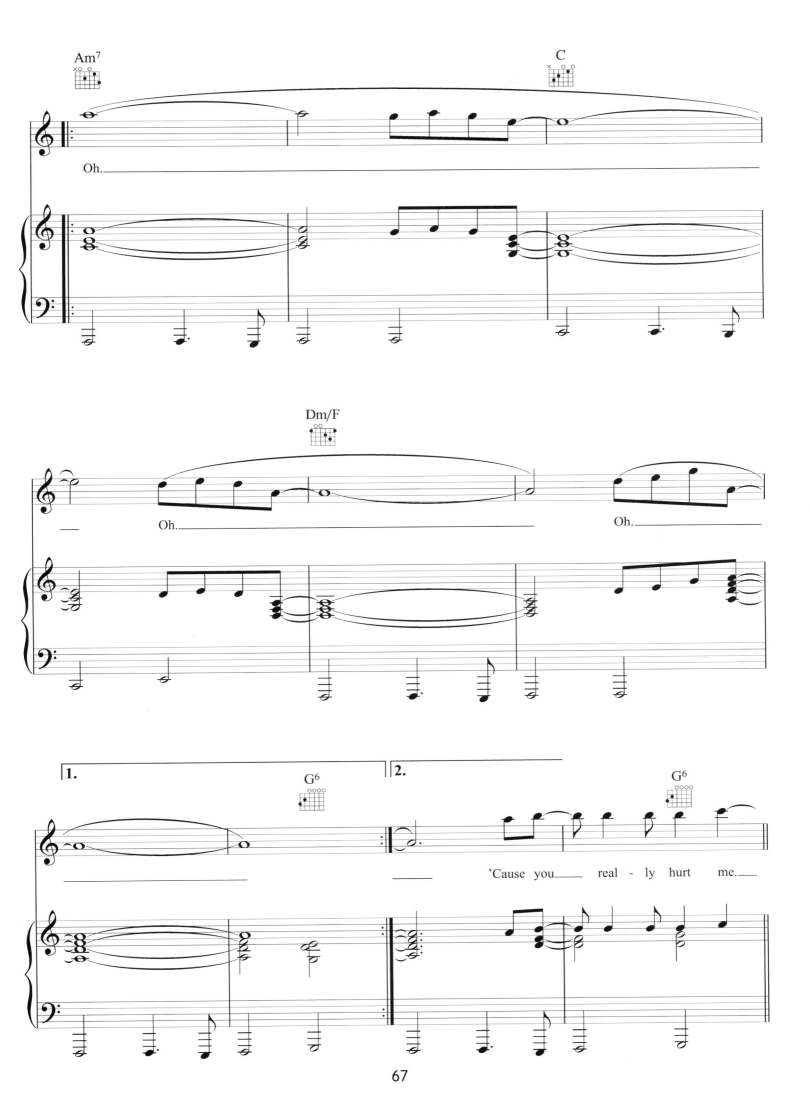

UP IN FLAMES

Words & Music by Chris Martin, Guy Berryman,
Jon Buckland, Will Champion

A HOPEFUL TRANSMISSION

Words & Music by Chris Martin, Guy Berryman, Jon Buckland, Will Champion & Brian Eno

DON'T LET IT BREAK YOUR HEART

Words & Music by Chris Martin, Guy Berryman,
Jon Buckland, Will Champion

Don't let it___ break your heart. *(echo)*

UP WITH THE BIRDS

Words & Music by Chris Martin, Guy Berryman, Jon Buckland, Will Champion & Brian Eno

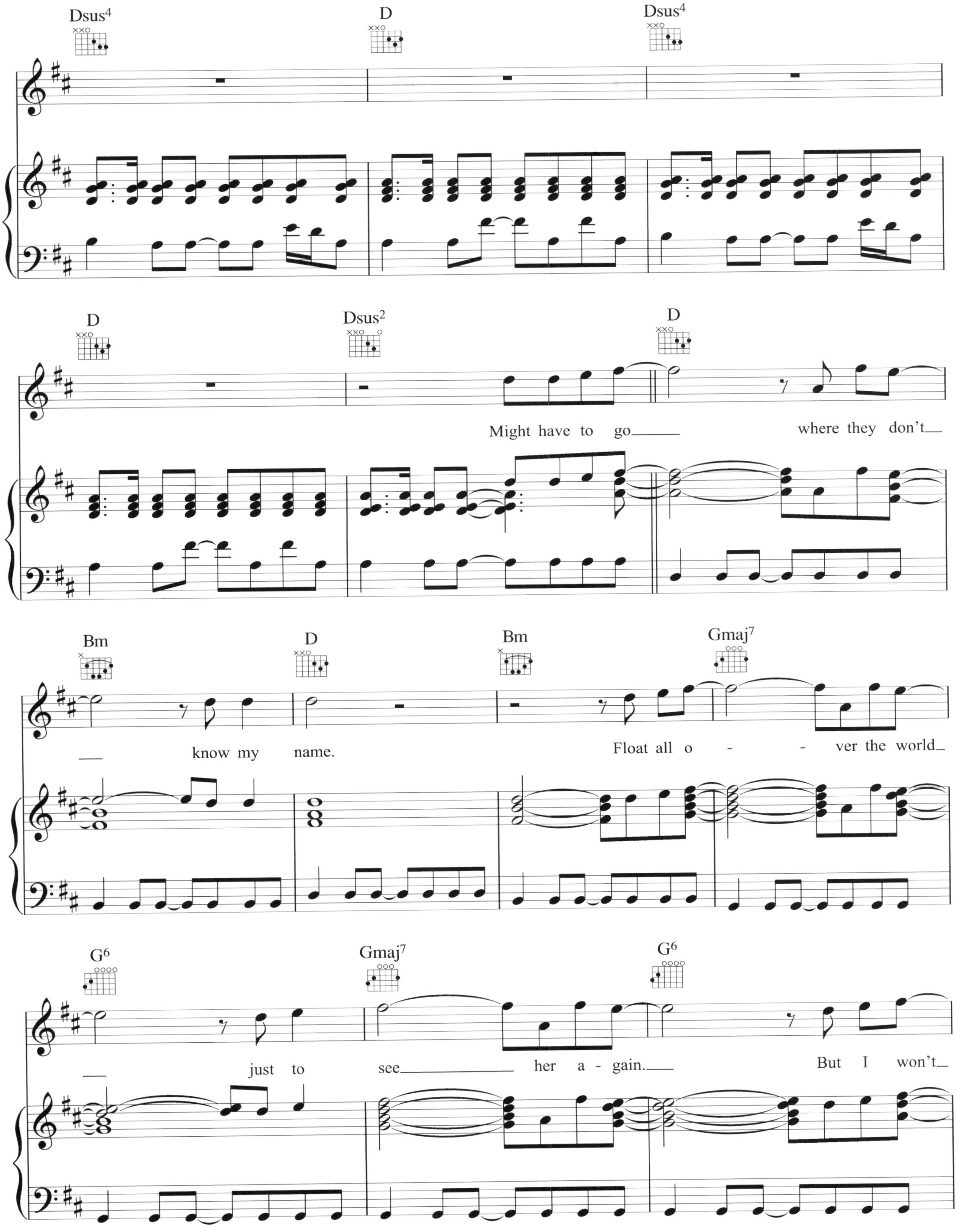

A sim-ple plot,____ Oh,____ yeah!____

123456789

ADDENDUM

The guitar chord boxes in this book are shown in conventional tuning (EADGBE).
This table shows the guitar tunings supplied by Chris Martin
to show how Coldplay perform these songs:

HURTS LIKE HEAVEN
EBEG♯BE (CAPO 6)

CHARLIE BROWN
EADGAD (CAPO 4)

US AGAINST THE WORLD
EADF♯AE (CAPO 3)

EVERY TEARDROP IS A WATERFALL
DADGAE

MAJOR MINUS
EADGBD

PRINCESS OF CHINA
EADGBE (CAPO 10)

U.F.O.
CGDGBD (CAPO 2)

UP WITH THE BIRDS
EADGBD (CAPO 7)